CW00394723

THE TRUE STORY OF
COWBOY HAT AND INGÉNUE

by
Maria Jastrzębska

Liquorice Fish
Books

L/FB 310

Published by Liquorice Fish Books, an imprint of Cinnamon Press, Meirion House, Tanygrisiau, Blaenau Ffestiniog, Gwynedd, LL41 3SU www.cinnamonpress.com/index.php/liquorice-fish-books/about

All rights reserved by the authors. The right of each contributor to be identified as the author of their work has been asserted by them in accordance with the Copyright, Designs and Patent Act, 1988.

Copyright © 2018 Maria Jastrzębska.

ISBN: 978-1-911540-03-8

British Library Cataloguing in Publication Data. A CIP record for this book can be obtained from the British Library.

All rights reserved. No part of this publication may be reproduced, stored in a retrieval system, or transmitted in any form or by any means, electronic, mechanical, photocopying, recording or otherwise without the prior written permission of the publishers. This book may not be lent, hired out, resold or otherwise disposed of by way of trade in any form of binding or cover other than that in which it is published, without the prior consent of the publishers.

This is a work of fiction. Names, characters, places, events and incidents are either drawn from the author's imagination or used fictitiously. Any resemblance to actual persons, living or dead, or to actual events is coincidental except when citing historical incidents.

Cover design Adam Craig. (Original images: tree skyline: Zhuangyouzhi/ Pixabay.com; rider: Skeeze/Pixabay.com; cowgirl: AdinaVoicu/Pixabay.com; town skyline: Adam Craig.)

Printed in Poland.

Cinnamon Press is represented in the UK by Inpress Ltd www.inpressbooks.co.uk and in Wales by the Welsh Books Council www.cllc.org.uk

Acknowledgements

Epigraph to Prologo from Antonio Machado courtesy of Patrick Early.

Epigraph to Primera Parte by Carolyn Forché from *Blue Hour* (Bloodaxe 2003). Reproduced with permission of Bloodaxe Books (*www.bloodaxebooks.com*).

Epigraph to Parte Final, "My Lady is No Lady" © 2018 by Anastasia Dunham-Parker-Brady. All rights reserved.

Epigraph for Segunda Parte from *Gunslinger*, p. 41 © 1989 by Edward Dorn. All rights reserved. Republished by permission of the copyright holder and the publisher Duke University Press (**www.dukeupress.edu**).

Grateful acknowledgement is made to the editors of the following journals and anthologies where some of these poems or versions of them first appeared: *Artemis, The Long Poem Magazine, Poetry London, Shearsman, Rattle* (USA), *Envoi, Molly Bloom, Sudden Prose — Prose Poems and Short Stories, Watermarks* (Frogmore Press 2017), *The Stony Thursday Book* (Ireland).

My thanks as always to Mimi Khalvati whose generosity to other poets is legendary and also to everyone at the Lewes Live Literature seminars. For their hospitality: to all at Almassera, in California to Danny and Charlotte Lubert and in Malaga to Rocio Claros and Javier Oliva where parts of this book were written. To poetry fellow travellers Janet Sutherland, John McCullough, Jackie Wills, Rob Hamberger, Robert Dickinson, Sue Robbins, Bernadette Cremmin for their encouragement.

For Deborah

and all the Cowboy Hats and Ingénues

THE TRUE STORY OF
COWBOY HAT AND INGÉNUE

Prólogo

'Caminante, son tus huellas
el camino, y nada mas;
caminante, no hay caminino…'

'Traveller, your footsteps alone
are the highway, there is no other;
traveller, there is no highway…'

Antonio Machado, Proverbiois y Cantares, Proverbs and Songs, from
A Voice in Time, A selection of poems by Antonio Machado, translated
by Patrick Early.

In the midst of everything, a cock crowing at the wrong time, dogs yelping in the distance, a wasp that wouldn't leave you alone, in the quiet and tedium of noon, someone in a truck leaned out saying: You wanna ride? I don't know where I'm going yet, you answered. Doesn't matter, get in. He or she was wearing a cowboy hat — that's what clinched it.

Flying across continents, massive white things, dipping in and out of the sky's turquoise reflection, over hillside and river, stone ruin and home, their wings cast shadows on the dust below. Rocio came running out of the kitchen. Look, everyone shouted, there they are.

Primera Parte

in which Ingénue finds Eldorado while elsewhere
in time la guerra *ravages the earth as it has*
always done

'a barnloft of horse dreams, with basin and bedclothes…
a memory through which one hasn't lived'

'On Earth' Carolyn Forché, *Blue Hour*

Nothing could have prepared you for this. A field, a village flattened, mashed up, gravy that's been spilled over the earth in grey, reddish-brown swirls. *We didn't think they'd ever come this far.*

The moment she arrives the air smells different. *Dame Blanche*, a giant black man leads the way, guiding her through underground tunnels which seem never-ending. Only half lit. She pushes through spiked turnstiles, heaves open iron doors, climbs up dank steps. When you reach the light you are in a clearing in which folk sit round bonfires. That's what she could smell. Or was it sweeter, more like frankincense? Some are playing fiddles, ukuleles, some whittling pipes, chewing something like tobacco and spitting into the fire. All of them wear Davey Crockett caps, except the woman in a cowboy hat who glances up, grinning. *Is everyone here a lesbian,* Ingénue asks. Cowboy Hat winks. *What about the men? Especially the men*, purrs Cowboy Hat, pulling the brim down over her eyes.

The lock-step doesn't link in the way she expected. It's continuous. She's never spun round a floor this fast. Later when Cowboy Hat takes her upstairs, her hands shake undoing the studs on her shotgun chaps. Hunger speaks through her fingertips so loudly she is afraid someone will hear.

What Cowboy Hat liked to say: *I'm kinda sceptical of a tree that is perfectly straight, seems or purports to be. It's a pretty good indication it's been staked to a vertical pole for a very long time. While this may look aes-thet-ically pleasing, it don't allow the tree to grow its own bending strength. Beware of* *pears. Check for ants in the bark. If it starts peeling, check for cracked or heaving soil.*

See, I can fix a leaking tap, mend a broken lamp, a chair, hell I can make a dovetail fit sweet and tight, cut a mortice and tenon so they gly-ide together, don't need no glue, I can make a drawer that fits in its carcase like a glove. Just don't ask me to wipe away your tears, don't ask me about… don't-even-make-me-say-it love.

Yipping and yelping, you rise on hind legs to box and rub noses, all fur and fluff, two prairie dogs, burrowing. You build your own home, a chamber for night, a chamber for winter and a listening post. Take in strays. Share every trout from the stream, every berry. You withstand hail and blizzards. When she swings up high to chop logs, the sweep of her arm just above her breast fells you all the way down.

Tell me about your hunger, Dame Blanche says. *The old hunger which never goes away. Its grip on you a strong arm marching you away from me even now. As people age, the hunger in them hardens. They end up bent double from carrying it like a boulder on their back and yearn for release. Hunger solidifies, it is a charred tree. The first time your hunger spoke it could play a tune and charm, now it only growls. Once your lover might have cradled you, sung you lullabies, now your hunger repulses her. When you call she sighs like someone climbing the stairs wearily carrying a bedpan or a transparent box of medication.*

A boy had hurried along the snow-covered road, his breath in puffs of steam, feet sinking in snow that was sticky like his grandmother's rice. The sky turned darker, a few smudges of light still left, golden as honey. She had told him not to be late, would pull his ear between her thumb and finger.

That's when he heard the first shot. Stopped at the top of the hill and saw the soldiers.

One by one, his grandmother, his father and brothers were led out only to fall onto the snow. His mother and sister were pulled away, lifted onto a truck. He noticed smoke still curling from their chimney. After he'd been sick and bent down to clean a little vomit on his shoe with a handful of snow, he turned and ran back the way he'd come as fast as he could along the snow-covered road.

The *Eldorado* **bar** is built on decking at one end of the giant marquee. It has its own sprung dance floor, saloon doors, booths with seats covered in red velvet or brocade. Kilim, tankas, saris, mestizo rugs — Dame Blanche calls them her *mappa mundi* — hang between mirrors and stained glass. Candelabras and crystal chimes swing down from a ceiling lined with what look like folds of pink fur.

Sitting the length of the bar this is what the women say: *La Pícara, Charlie, of course, then Lizard Lil. Wouldn't give up the lifestyle. Broke Cowboy Hat's heart. Nah, she ain't got a heart. Just a lively you know what! Remember that bronco rider? Blue Somebody? Tranzubztantiation. Knife thrower? Like a house on fire. Only Cowboy Hat couldn't stand the heat. Tranz never held a grudge. Scary one — changed her name to Prairie Flower? Prickly pear more like. Dame… Oogh no. Business. Strictly. Besides… Back when. Helped Cowboy after she… What was her name? Sophie? Sally! A beauty. Ho ran off. All Cowboy's savings. No brains when it comes to women. I always liked Mai. Yeah, she had class. And the acrobat. What? You kicked me, that hurts.* Out of nowhere it seems or anywhere perhaps, Dame Blanche slides silently towards them from behind the bar. Their heads all turn together. ¿Que desea? *What'll it be?* says Dame Blanche to Ingénue, who has just walked in.

That night Ingénue can't sleep. Stares at the hump of Cowboy Hat's back, a whale rising and falling in an ocean of endless dark blue. She's curled in on herself, sleeping like a baby. With every thought a little harpoon hurtling towards her, Ingénue wills Cowboy Hat to wake up. Some nights Cowboy Hat spins round. Then the sky fills with stars. *Only one thing can help you get to sleep now*, she exhales.

Dust settles as the truck drives away. The dogs stop barking, lazily the youngest of them attempts to catch the wasp which flies too far to chase. The dog rolls onto its side on a hot stone step, falls asleep. Sun burns its fur, burns the grass and stones. Shutters are closed, wood knocking, wood on wood. Knock three times. For health, for prosperity and in love for luck.

Did I hear that right? Dame Blanche casts Cowboy Hat a sidelong glance, long as the longest river coiling through swamps and full of the idle silhouettes of gators who sun themselves in dappled light, ready to snap off your limbs with the blink of one eye. *I jus' meant, what if there's someone I'm s'pposed to meet? Later on? Because you said can I think of anything that's not perfect about her and when she smiles she's got this one tooth trips you over, bust in a fight or maybe it grew that way, she won't tell, in an otherwise perfect row, one crooked tooth.*

Increíble, *you ain't sure if she's the one on account of her* dientes? *You sure you wouldn't prefer a hoss?*

Stepping outside for a cigarette, *I really hope, I hope, hope, hope it works out for them,* says Dame Blanche, *a kiss of the teeth, a shake of beaded locks heavy as curtains. I mean they're hunkering down now, leaning into one another like the perfectly jointed timber sides of a shack, a pyramid fire built to blaze, pointing tall into the freezing night, but I've seen it* *all come falling down, cold ash in their oats in the morning, scraped and swilled round a billy can.*

Is it true *you know how to conceal a razor-blade in your mouth?* Ingénue asks. *Could you show me how it's done?* Dame Blanche is tying French beans to a stake in her garden behind Eldorado. *That should hold them. Aha and spit it out at an unsuspecting target, movin' or otherwise. Well, if you were Black the bouncers always searched you but they never thought to look there.*

The trick is to loosen the tongue so it floats like a little ship bobbing under the roof of your mouth. Open your lips. See, there's a tiny stove on board from which smoke coils, a black flag's fluttering from the mast and all the passengers are gazing at the immensity of another world outside. From your open mouth, let your breath drift like the smoke. Effortlessly. You don't need to blow or puff, it will leave by itself just as sweet, new air breezes gently in, the whole transaction unfolding and continuing for as long as you live.

Now imagine your breath forming rings like those a smoker blows through their lips, only you *don't have to do a thing. The rings slip out by themselves and just as they leave your mouth so do the animals. One by one they leave the sinking little ship of your tongue: tigers and lions or great* bisontes, *maybe even a giraffe, dancing bears and monkeys chase each other, their trainers in top hats — helpless to stop them — as they scramble towards the rings. Rats, of course, rats, scorpions and cockroaches too, and long-legged spiders which have lodged inside you far too long. They jump into the shallows around your tongue, clear the ridge of your bottom teeth, climbing over your lip. As soon as they leap through the rings of breath floating from your mouth, they're gone. You could say: evaporated.*

What about the hard kisses? Sometimes they follow the butterfly kisses: if she doesn't feel the same way you will surely die. Hare-brained, almost harsh, hard up, foolhardy, hard on their luck, they push your tongue into each chink of intimation, nudge right through, find who she and you might be on the other side.

But the butterfly kisses, eyelash to eyelash, are equally foolish. Silky, hopeful. The two of you, feet tucked under, napping, small. Cocooned together. Marooned together. Morning, noon and night and each afternoon you want to swoon together.

Feeling drunk, you force yourself to go for a glass of water, lurching from side to side like someone crossing the length of a train, holding out your arms for balance.

On a day without any breeze, the Commander is strolling across the sleepy square when he hears children chasing a round-faced child, *Gordita, Gordita Chocinita* they call. He asks the priest who has become his interpreter what it means and on learning it means piggy girl he tells his henchmen to find the child.

That afternoon the villagers cannot believe their eyes as the men, having built a huge fire in the centre of the square, hang the child trussed up like an animal over its flames. The child screams. The people plead and shout. The Commander inclines his head and the men fire a round of shots above the crowd to silence them. *But it's you who are responsible for this,* he drawls, *you are the ones who named her Chocinita in the first place.* His voice carries in the stillness like smoke rising lazily on a day without any breeze.

What's on your mind? asks Ingénue. Nothing. You see, that's what I mean. Why won't you talk to me? No, I really mean Nothing. Nada. Niets. Ni?. Nothing. How long's a pause?

If Nothing can be measured then it exists as surely as all the clutter. Mostly, everyone's scared of it but what if you could just touch it, would it burn your finger, would it taste like snow? How can you tell which is background and foreground? If you didn't yank it out like buttonweed. What if it was the true flower opening right in front of you but you never saw it. I wanna know what falls between every guitar note, each atom, between you and me. Is there purity? Not a stopping place but something — Nothing — that endures in and out of earth and space. Imagine we're two drops of rain snaking down, smudging a window.

Everyone knows her blue eyes saved her. The soldier aiming his gun at her expected them to be brown like other villagers', was surprised by a pair of blue eyes as steady as his aim, as blue as his own. He hesitated for only a moment.

Mercedes' grandfather, her mother and her sister — the one who left to become a nun, changing her name to Asunta — all from the mountain village had the same blue eyes. Not sea green like lowlanders but periwinkle and midnight blue. They used to ride down on donkeys selling water melon but the tourists gave them bigger tips to have their picture taken. The tourists liked to stand next to the villagers and their donkeys in the pictures and her grandfather saved enough to buy a plot of land.

As the soldier hesitated her older brother ran out and shot him with a rifle they kept for hunting shrews and rabbits. The soldier wasn't dead. One foot was still shaking and he groaned aloud. Her brother hit him over the head with a shovel till his rasping stopped. Mercedes helped drag the body out of sight. They buried him in a dip behind the olive groves, covered the grave with stones so vultures wouldn't draw attention to the spot.

Look Mama, some *of them open like flowers.* Rocio has turned her face to the wall. Lying on the narrow divan, complaining of a headache. The bangs hammer inside her body, not in the street. *I had enough flames and explosions to last me a lifetime,* she mutters. *But they're so pretty.* Something in her daughter's voice melts her resolve and she lets herself be led by the hand onto the balcony. The sky is streamed with colour. And though she covers her ears with her hands, she is soon sighing with everyone else. A little 'oh' escapes her lips as the sky lights up first with a giant gold palm, then a pair of shimmering red lips which seem to blow her back a kiss, more stars, then red hearts which leap so swiftly past her above winding streets, rooftops and spires.

Helplessly, Cowboy Hat watches as Ingénue places the knife between her teeth and dives. Gone below the jet green surface of the water — some call it Hooker's green but she doesn't care for that name — gone so long Cowboy Hat curses, pulling off her leathers. At last Ingénue's head bobs up, she is waving. She has speared a fish which she holds triumphantly over her head. Her voice echoes between the rocks on either side of the creek and she won't stop chirping and grunting like some old frog or a creaky wheel as she splashes, diving and surfacing. Even purring in the green water.

Cowboy Hat looks around. As she lowers herself in slowly, slipping on the muddy bank, she curses again. An icy wave slaps her belly — *Maybe this was a mistake.* But as she opens her arms, the silky water wraps itself around her. She propels her tired body through reeds, feeling in the shallows the sudden warmth of sun, shivering where bottlebrush and swamp oak cast their shadows. For a moment her limbs dissolve, weariness melts away and she lets the current carry her towards Ingénue. They tussle and Cowboy Hat swallows mouthfuls of river water before Ingénue, slippery and sleek, wins, as she usually does. Biting Cowboy Hat on the nose harder than she expected.

Squeezes her thighs around her. *Isn't it clever, how hot your body stays on the inside?* Cowboy Hat throws back her head, gurgles, squeals, chirps.

Father Ignatio, who put his penis in the boys' mouths and told them it was a sacrament, was spared. He told the soldiers he would lead them to a secret hiding place in the olive groves where the Bishop had buried gold chalices. Above them, the sun burned in the sky and a pair of bee eaters flashed green wings across the valley. As the soldiers marched into the hills with him, they came under enemy fire. The other side, seeing a man of the cloth, killed his captors and freed him.

Most of the nuns were killed by the first soldiers, except for Sister Asunta who escaped and was hidden by Claribel, who not only gave her clothes — a blue skirt and a blouse with a bright pattern of tulips and lilies — but also lipstick so that the soldiers would never know she was a nun. When the second regiment of soldiers marched into the village, they raped both Claribel and Sister Asunta and would not believe she was a nun or else they did not care.

We're closed, honey, says Dame Blanche, not looking up as she drags a crate of beers across the floor. *Oh it's you, here help me with these.* Cowboy Hat has slipped in through an untied flap. *You know how long it takes to get your own cabin. I made the sleigh bed with my own hands, sweet walnut, then those sheets she wanted! Had to be Aegyptian Black, cost all my wages. And now she's taken to sleeping out the front. I mean right outside in the clearing, not in a hammock on the porch. 'I want to catch the stars fallin,' she says. Tells me a coyote woke her up last night, licking her eyelashes.*

Where is she? Sal, Lil or whatever her name is, Ingénue demands. It has taken her a day of riding in circles, asking strangers the way to reach the clearing. *I'm talking to you!* Cowboy Hat looks up and waves her chisel slowly in the direction of the surrounding birches. *Be my guest, look around.* Ingénue is so tired she crouches down at the edge of the porch, won't go a step nearer. *And it never occurred to you to mention where you were going...* Is there is any point speaking? In the long pause, she thinks she can make out the buzz of a bumble bee and the tap, tap of a woodpecker. Will she ever get used to the silence? Cowboy Hat blows shavings from the curved piece of wood in her hands. The crease of a smile returns to the corners of her eyes. *I thought I'd work a little on this rocking chair for you, it was gonna be* una sorpresa.

When they kiss, her heart leaps into her mouth bold as a new green frog. It's a kiss fizzy as lemonade. It tingles from tip top to heel and toe till her bum fluff stands on end. Electric as a storm. A kiss that kick-ball changes everything, starts the whole daffadowndillydo spring till it jump cuts to another story, years down the line.

A word in the ear of the news editor from the bishop meant nothing of this was reported, despite photographs of the cortege, citations of the priest's courage in war, praise for his work with orphans. But soft as thistledown rumours spread, carried by the wind of conversations on street corners and blown into cafés and stalls with the opening of awnings.

No one knows who they were — a man and an unusually tall dark-skinned woman, her face unseen behind a black mantilla. They walked so solemnly up the aisle to the open coffin of Father Ignatius that the bishop did not even pause in his eulogy. Heads bowed they knelt first, laid something in the coffin, a spray of flowers, a photograph, surely, and withdrew to the back of the church, disappearing into the crowd by the door.

As the service ended and the congregation snaked past the coffin to pay their last respects, there were gasps. Intakes of breath followed by whispers. Somebody should have done something but no one dared reach a hand into the coffin. Afterwards they disagreed. Some said it was polished wood, others swore it was excrement glazed with egg white or (someone else argued) semen, in any case frosted with sugar so that it shone — the small sculpture of a penis in the priest's mouth.

Tranquila. **Dame Blanche** is used to hearing both sides, and often more, to every question. *Let's sit outside, amor, we'll have un café, un cigarillo* she invites her, though Ingénue has already thrown herself into a rocking chair, curling up at once like a cat: *How can she be so sweet one moment and gone the next? Leaving before I'm awake. Doesn't say where she's going or when she's coming back. What am I supposed to do?*

She'll be back. She thinks if she keeps riding she's going to come across her little girl and there's no telling her any different. Ingénue has not taken her eyes off Dame Blanche's face. Doesn't notice the mug flying out of her own fingers onto the porch. It could turn into a bird flapping its wings — she wouldn't see. Instead it plummets, falling soundlessly till it cracks on the ground and the milk spills. *Uh oh,* says Dame Blanche, tapping old bearberry and red willow bark from her pipe against the heel of one boot to start a new smoke. *I guess Cowboy Hat never told you.*

Get up, he yells but she knows as soon as she stands he will knock her down again. *Think,* she tells herself knowing with each blow, each fall, she grows weaker. She has already looked round for a weapon but there is nothing in the yard. Only the plough and tractor parts too heavy for her to lift. *Get up!* With what is left of her strength, she hurls herself at his ankle and bites down hard. He curses, surprised by such sharp pain. Without thinking, tries to free his leg while she clings on like a rabid dog. He is roaring but she feels something slacken and suddenly he is losing balance. Whipping her body round, her teeth still sunk into his leg, she pushes with both heels behind the kneecap of his other leg. He topples. She rolls away and hears a crack as his head hits the edge of the plough. A stream of blood inches its way towards her. Cowboy Hat doesn't know if he is still alive or already dead, doesn't know what frightens her more.

What Cowboy Hat remembers: *Is it true you dress in men's clothes? Is that why they call you Cowboy Hat? What's an* abominatión? They are standing behind one of the old redwoods, its trunk easily broad enough to hide them. On that day every effort is made to impress the visiting *dignitarios* and *benefactores* strolling through the grounds. There are tables of almond cakes, *piñata* for the children. Cowboy Hat is supposed to be helping carry glasses of mint tea and jugs of white wine. They always know how to find each other.

It's easier to ride in leathers and they call me a lot of names but the one which matters most is Mama, that's who I am — tu Mama. She shifts from one foot to the other in *falda plisada* and flowery blouse, crouches down to the child's eye level. *We don't have much time, I want you to keep this* pañuelo, *tie it round your neck to remember me by. Don't go, Mama.* Another time: *Don't grow old, Mama.* And the last time they meet: *When I grow up I'll ride the world from end to end and find you.*

Rub a finger of lard into your labiolitos *to ease the friction, smear the juice of* granadas *into your pubic hair and down each thigh. It will make him think it's your time of month,* the older ones advise Rocio. *Fight back with elbows and teeth, these are your natural weapons. No, don't struggle, don't move a muscle, it only arouses them more.* They can't agree. *Wriggle quicksilver when he relaxes his hold,* baberita mi. *Look,* her aunt points at the sky through the small window, *have the squirrels nested down? Are the geese flying low? Can you see a halo of diamonds around the moon? Pray snow falls tonight and cuts off the mountain pass, then the soldiers won't find us.*

What Dame Blanche told Ingénue: *You know, the first time Cowboy Hat dressed in a shirt with silver collar tips and a black horse hair bolo tie she'd saved up for, her mother slapped her saying wait till your father comes home. Cowboy Hat never waited that long. Cowboy Hat don't talk about it much but I figure something had already happened. Anyhow when she ran away from home, she realised she was pregnant. Back then you didn't have a choice. The nuns took her baby to that orphanage, named after the priest. And of course it was worse with Cowboy Hat being who she was. The priests said she was an abomination, not fit to raise a child. Only there was one nun who befriended Cowboy Hat. Sister Asunta told her someone had once helped* her *but wouldn't say more. She even lent her clothes and lipstick, though how a nun had come by those I couldn't tell you. That's how, till Sister Asunta died, Cowboy Hat got to see her kid. But now — well it's been a few years, no one will tell Cowboy Hat anything. She gets it in her head the girl is out there looking for her so she rides and rides the tallgrass prairie.*

Segunda Parte

*in which Cowboy Hat and Ingénue set off on
a quest as pointless as it is miraculous, as all
journeys are, the past on their heels, while the
future — whether beguiled or envious, who can
tell? — peers at them*

'How far is it Claude?
                    Across
two states
of mind, saith the Horse.'

Edward Dorn, *Gunslinger*

How can anyone *live here?* The streets are so narrow, stripey underpants and white sheets hanging from one balcony get tangled in the red brassieres and silk embroidered scarves of the window opposite; tradescantia and pelargonium send out tendrils and shoots to each others' window boxes, forming a dark canopy above the already shaded street. *They don't, they sleep walk. But how do they squeeze between the walls of the houses? They just eat less than us and their expectations haven't grown sky high.*

Don't tell me *they eat too much here* says Ingénue when they reach a city whose streets are so wide you can't see across from one side to another. That night from their room in a glass and concrete cube on the outskirts of the city she looks up into the sky but there are no stars.

Peering now, Cowboy Hat can see each doll on the dresser has been mutilated in some way and then patched up. The cloth ones have large sprawling stitches in their arms and the plastic ones have bandages with streaks of red paint dripping from their limbs. *This explains a lot,* she whistles. *I can't believe your folks kept all this stuff. My Mama chucked everything out. Mind we moved around a lot, on account of when the bailiffs got too close.* Ingénue's mother has followed them into the room. She has mistaken Cowboy Hat's whistle for shock at the small wounds and speaks quickly: *She always wanted to look after everything, I mean, there was that time she stole an owlet from its nest and hid it in her room, do you remember darling?*

Why would you *want to leave behind the only safety you ever found to come with me?* says Cowboy Hat. *Because if we don't look round the next corner we'll lose it anyway. It will grow stagnant like swamp water. I was never good at standing still. Also it can't be* una enorme sorpresa — *as you put it — that I love you.*

Not bad, **says** Cowboy Hat watching as Ingénue cleans and guts the river trout they have caught. *I guess I learnt something at medical school after all, huh? Was that when you were engaged to Roberto? Oh sly fox, storing that up, who told you? Let's just say me and your papa had a little man to woman chat. What else did he say? He told me you could have been in a lucrative practice by now, wanted to know how much you could earn, so I said: it don't really work like that. I tried to explain the bartering.* Cowboy Hat is slicing green zebra tomatoes. *I bet he loved that. Yeah, I could tell he weren't too keen. Anyhow he told me about the yacht, how Roberto made you a gift and you wouldn't take it. Did he also tell you that Roberto announced to everybody that we were engaged before I'd agreed? Well didn't you want to marry him? It had crossed my mind but I hadn't decided and he went right ahead. What happened? I didn't accept his stupid yacht. Just out of interest what kind of sloop was it? Oh honestly! You're as stupid as my brothers, all they did was quiz me about the frigging boat, how many knots could she do, how much water did she draw as if that were relevant.*

Cowboy Hat spears the wild asparagus they have picked at the edge of the woods that lead down to the shore. She dips each tip in olive oil and salt ready to roast on their fire as the giant orange sun teeters on the horizon about to roll into the ocean. *You know I'm never going to be able to make you an offer like that. Hell I barely make enough to live on myself.* Ingénue glares: *Now you sound like my father* y no es atractivo, no en absoluto! She cleans off her knife before putting it back in its sheath and, not caring if she kicks sand over Cowboy Hat and their meal, strides off.

After a little while she stops to look back and shout: *Why does everyone treat me as if I need taking care of? I've always paid my own way. I worked in a goddamn zoo mucking out the cages all through college so I wouldn't have to ask my family for a penny. How dare you of all people treat me like some porcelain doll? I bet that's not how you handled Lizard Lil. Or should I be putting that in the present? How you still handle Lizard Lil?* Cowboy Hat stares at her but before she can think of a reply, Ingénue shouts again*: We were going to share* una deliciosa comida *on this beach and now it's ruined. Why do you ruin everything?* Ingénue turns on her heel and is gone.

A bear is riding a bicycle around the market square. It wears a red flat cap and a name tag dangles from its neck. In bold letters it says: *My name is Pimpo — Have the Ride of Your Life!* Attached to the back of the bike is a little cart. Five or six children at a time can climb onto the cart to be taken round the stalls and into one of the streets which circle the market. Every child who sees the bear begs for a ride. The parents find themselves walking over to the trainer, a man with a face so tattooed you can hardly see his eyes, who smokes one cheroot after another, chewing the ends and spitting them out. *You gotta ask the bear,* he says and tugs a chain on the bear's neck. As he does so the bear nods its huge, brown head. The children climb on and to the parents' dismay the man gives the chain one last yank and then lets go. The bear rides off by itself, the children squealing with delight. *I thought this kind of thing was illegal,* says Ingénue. *Not round here,* mutters Cowboy Hat.

One hot day, around noon, just as the market traders are starting to pack up their baskets, one or two calling out a last drop in prices on unsold tomatoes, quinces, turkeys and *jamon*, and as the flies hover over everything, Pimpo sets off on another ride round the square. You can see the bear's red cap disappearing round a corner. The parents are waiting to wave a greeting to the children. They look for the man with the chain but he is nowhere to be seen. A stall-holder, packing up crates of lemons, shrugs and points to the nearest bar. The adults split into two groups and run down either end of the street which circles the square but the bear riding a bicycle has gone.

Who in hell's been talking to you about Lizard Lil? Who? The whole of Eldorado talks of nothing except your exes and there's enough to fill una enciclopedia. Lizard Lil was good to me once and I don't forget a kindness. Kindness? Is that what you call it? So why have you been visiting her again? She has contacts. She's friends with the madrotas and they know all the comings and goings. Every judge, every politician, policeman and priest winds up in the zonas de tolerancia and they tell the women every secret in the world. I thought she might know something about the kid. I swear it, I swear that was all.

They are dozing, entwined in the warm sand, when the sound of softly approaching footsteps rouses them. Cowboy Hat raises herself up on one elbow, lightly draping the cotton hammam towel Dame Blanche gave them over their bodies. *It's one of the mariposas* she whispers. *Excuse the intrusion ladies,* a tanned man in a golden silk loin cloth steps towards them, *but I thought I should warn you, the creep with that sad excuse of a telephoto lens for a phallic symbol is on the prowl again and I think it's a sight of you he's after, rather than us. Oh?* says Ingénue. *Let's give him a sighting of us then.* She shakes off the towel and pulling Cowboy Hat up by the hand jumps to her feet. *This I need to see,* their new friend says following the women, who run naked, yelling and screaming, over the sand dunes straight towards the man with his camera.

Two rows of white houses hang like loose teeth from the sky, a gap between them. When the mist lifts, Ingénue gulps down her mint tea, grabbing Cowboy Hat's hand. They follow a curve in the road till they reach the top of the rocks, where half the town perches on the cliff's edge. Its mirrored twin looks back at them from across the ravine. Further along, a bridge has been built to join up the two sides of the town but, where they stand, there is only a drop, sharp as the intake of breath.

Don't lean over, says Cowboy Hat. *Soldiers beaten with sticks and* mayales *were dragged from the Plaza of the Ayuntamiento and hurled down from this cliff. People say their spirits,* espíritus de los lamentos, *rising from the dry riverbed will catch you by the ankles and drag you all the way down.*

Our own people did this? says Ingénue. *You gotta understand what those people lived through to make them fierce like that,* whispers Cowboy Hat. *Understand?* Ingénue spits on the ground. *If they could use horsewhips and scythes on their enemies they're no better than them. Understand? I'd like to understand how yesterday here is tomorrow somewhere else, how beavers know when to store sticks of quaking aspen before winter, hauling branches with their teeth, or what makes the heart stop and start, but not this, I never want to understand this.*

The door is heavy to push open but, when at last they succeed, they find another door with a grille, almost like a confessional, only the mesh covers the entire door. Behind it stands a woman, at least they think she is a woman, sculpted breasts bare. She is dressed in feather chaps — *Goose quill*, murmurs Cowboy Hat — and only her eyes are visible, nose and mouth concealed by a ladderwork of gold zips on a gimp mask. *You can't come in naked like that,* she rasps and Ingénue imagines her wrinkling her nose under the gleaming metal and leather helmet. Ingénue stares at the doorkeeper's breasts but Cowboy Hat has pulled out a roll of banknotes. *We'll hire the masks.* The door rattles open.

Waiters — or waitresses — some in kilts, others draped in everything from silk organza and chainmail to barnacles and sea bladders, balance trays of drinks higher than the horns on their shoulders as they sashay past. Perched on their heads, alligators look back down their snouts at the two visitors, tails flick from backsides. *The sex rooms are just round the corner,* the doorkeeper calls after them in a hoarse voice.

Big blue patches of snow — or is it grey ash fall — on something or someone not moving. Are they doves alighting on the shoulders of a saint, perching on a statue? From a distance it's hard to make out the outline of an old man on the bench as, one by one, pigeons settle on his arms, his head. Cowboy Hat and Ingénue are strolling between rows of plane trees. As they draw nearer, they see the man is not dead but eating a bread roll, soft as a cloud, which he tears with his hands. His face where it's visible under a white beard is leathery, red — an unexpected San Nicolás in summer. Round his mouth, the beard and moustache are yellowed, his faded jacket splattered with dried, chalky guano, his small eyes red. If he notices the birds, he does nothing to shoo them away. They perch on his head, peck at the roll in his hands, picking crumbs out of his beard. *Coo, coo, coo, coo, coo.* He doesn't seem to mind sharing his bread with them, opens his mouth for a bite and the birds are about swoop in to snatch the bread when a piece drops on the ground. Momentarily distracted, they hop onto the pavement, walk round his knapsack and the plastic bag with his carryout, then hop back.

Cowboy Hat is tugging at Ingénue's hand to walk quicker. *What is it,* querida? *Who was that man?* Ingénue tries to read her face. It is only once they are out of the park that Cowboy Hat speaks: *That was my father. Was that one of your jokes? No. He's seasonal. Out every summer. Winters in the subways. You never talk to him? Not anymore. Besides what would we talk about? I don't know how to coo and you've seen the company he keeps.*

What Cowboy Hat said: *The idea is to show compassion. To soothe their wild cries of ha ha. Waste nothing. Even bones left by the griffon vultures get ground down and offered up again, this time to crows and hawks in waiting. Sometimes if there's only one body, the birds don't realise it's there and have to be im-por-tuned to come. Imagine if they didn't feast that day, imagine being turned down by* carroñeros.

I've seen bodies left on a hillside, though once at dawn I saw they floated someone on a raft of straw downriver. I s'ppose the dead don't care. I always thought I'd be cremated but it comes to the same if you're laid out on a long, smooth rock.

What Cowboy Hat didn't say: *Truth is I think about dying all the time except when I think of something else. Why would I tell her that? What would I say? Apart from anything else it brings bad luck. I can't tell her I see us on that rock. That I'm up there among unbidden, circling* criaturas, *preying on myself, on our own bodies tangled in sleep or sweet desires. Build barns and cabins, window frames, plane and wax a door so it fits exactly, so you can shut it behind you and keep* las criaturas del aire *out. Or just keep movin', ridin', your mind on something else.*

As soon as they arrive in a new place they play the game. Cowboy Hat says she can always tell: *If someone's lying, catch their eye and you'll know. See those two in the alcove listening to the guitarist — on the low cushions? Even when the lights go down they don't touch, don't lean against one another lightly as friends might do without arousing suspicion. But there's a* *hidden ease as they sit side by side, something shifting between their two outlines, a current fluctuating through negative space, as if a never-ending stream of butterflies fluttered between their thighs.*

There are places along a river where you don't need to move your arms or kick your legs to swim. It's enough to float on your back and let the current underneath the dazzling surface carry you. Look up into the sky until the clouds move with you. Suddenly, out of the corner of your eye, quick as shadow and gone before you know it, you'll see a heron flapping its wide slate-grey wings above you. Almost out of sight it will land, upstream, perching on a rock that juts out of the dark green water. Only the wind in the bulrushes and the splash of fish leaping will make any sound. The sun will warm your face. You will be weightless, like old driftwood, fallen blossom, water itself.

What Ingénue remembers is being wedged between her mother and father, barely able to move. In spite of that her mother says: *Try to keep still.* It's the same every week. Everyone shuffles and coughs until the altar boy's bell rings, summoning them to silence. It's so hot and quiet she's sure she's going to suffocate, when she notices it. First the fly lands on a hat a few rows in front of her, diving among purple flowers. Against the dark background of the hat its folded wings shimmer. Ingénue counts colours of the rainbow... red, orange... indigo. It almost gets trapped in the black tulle which cascades from the rim of the hat and after pedalling with all six legs, like an early pilot from her *Popular Aviation*, defying gravity and scepticism, it triumphs — taking off just in time to land on the priest's bald head as he lifts the holy sacrament in both hands. He'll have to let go with one hand in order to swat the fly. Ingénue inches forward on the kneeler waiting to see what he'll do. Everyone else in the pew, even her brothers, has bowed their head. But in the aisle opposite, a girl with a red side plait has seen the fly too and, as their eyes meet, the girl's look catches her off-guard with a sweetness that carries force equal to a well-aimed punch.

The creek boasts only one shop. Wood-built and whitewashed every spring, it perches on the cliff edge. You can buy pigs' ears, horn buttons and a balm for poisonwood there, as well as *albahaca* in season. Outside there's a row of wooden mailboxes, bleached by sun, weathered by rains. For some reason no one bothers to paint the boxes any more, so it's hard to tell if anyone still uses them. You could collect letters here and no one would care. If an old nun climbed the hill to the shop to buy *achiote* seeds and opened one of the boxes, no one would pay her attention. They'd think she was helping some illiterate person to read and write letters home.

After only glimpsing the peaks between bars of red fir and sugar pine, after walking, heads down for so long, picking out violets and blue eyed mary's in mud and dust, after treading ground carpeted with needles and cones and being startled by the pointed, red bracts of snow plants which thrive with the least sun (where the trees part like weighted curtains) they are dazzled by the open hand of the world — the jagged chain of giant mountains, royal flush of light and rock.

Is this what birds feel? says Ingénue. *Living higher up than us? Don't stop, we gotta keep movin',* says Cowboy Hat, *or it'll get too cold.* Ingénue isn't listening. Though it hurts, she cranes her neck to look up. Nimble as a chipmunk, her gaze runs up along the thick bark of trees so tall her gaze soon tumbles down again. Dizzy and short of breath, she strains to see the black crowns of the trees and above them stars whose stillness makes her heart beat even faster.

Like a jackdaw flapping dark wings, her mother swoops down shrieking: *Stupid girl, what have you done?* Rocio stands surrounded by the broken pieces of the tureen, *caldo* soup running green in different directions across the flagstones. Her mother slaps her so hard she topples over and a shard of terra cotta cuts her bare leg. Soon a red stream trickles across to meet the green one, which now turns browner on its journey between strewn leaves of *col rizada* and diced potatoes. Stopped by a sudden large sprig of *tomillo* it forms a pool until it finds a way to flow around it. Rocio opens and closes her mouth but no sound comes out. *Who do you think will pay for this? You? Or maybe he will?* her mother carries on shouting. *Shall we ask your dear daddy? Shall we break all the plates just for fun?* If Rocio were a little fish she could dive into the blood and soup, swim far away to the ocean where no one would find her.

In order to train a bear you need to separate a cub from its mother. First a hole is burnt through the nose at the base of the muzzle. A rope or ring is inserted through the wound and forced out. Chains or ropes can be attached to the ring. Even though bears weigh around 350 pounds, once they are grown, they can now be disciplined with only the slightest tug. To teach a bear to dance it must be led onto sheets of glowing metal, sometimes hot embers, while music is played. To escape the pain, a bear will alternate lifting first one paw then the other. If this is repeated over and over, as soon as it hears the music the bear will automatically raise its paws even when it's no longer standing on hot metal. Some trainers say they learned their skills as young boys, watching how adults taught the animals. Others declare love for each of the cubs.

Inside the truck there was almost no light except for the smallest crack in the metal shutter doors, which enabled her to guess if it was day or night. The drivers had shouted that they were not to try opening the doors when the truck stopped or they could be apprehended, maybe shot. They had stopped only once in a forest and been allowed to relieve themselves at night. A signal of knocks from the driver's cabin had been arranged to let them know when a border patrol was being approached. Inside the truck there was nowhere they could relieve themselves, so someone suggested they make one side of the truck their latrine and all sleep on other. They dragged some cylinders and boxes across to create a divide but sometimes the urine trickled across to the other side anyway.

The clatter of the truck and passing traffic were something she quickly got used to. Much harder were the heat and thirst as no one had brought enough water for such a long journey. On the third morning, as she imagined it, even over the stench inside the lorry she could smell something different. The smell of brine. Ocean. They had reached the ocean.

Oh, oh! **cries** Ingénue, when she sees two humpbacks breach, shattering the ocean's glass blue sheen. *Where?* shouts Cowboy Hat. *How come I never see them and you do, even when you're driving?*

Eagles flank their pathway, swooping down alongside the truck, which levitates above the tarmac's haze. Ingénue rests an arm on the rolled down window. She purses her lips and whistles to the birds. Cowboy Hat opens one eye. Eagles alight on her lover's arm, snatching morsels, of *quesadilla* from her open hand. *I was gonna eat that,* mutters Cowboy Hat then goes back to sleep.

The ocean is a blue lake of concentration. It sucks in clouds. Swallowed whole, the clouds are snowy peaks and mountain glitter, black coal. The ocean is an ice rink, waves hairline fractures. And fishing boats are lovers, casting a net between them.

Isn't it clever how they draw maps of the ocean when there's nothing there? Look how bare the horizon is. Just stars, which you can't even see some nights. No wonder they imagined sea pigs and seven-footed worms lived in the water. Did you know they drew human horse-fish as well ordinary mermen? Ingénue leans out over the railings to peer down. *Give me a few minutes, darlin',* says Cowboy Hat, *a few goddamn minutes.* She stands huddled, holding her belly as if it might fall out of her body and roll across the deck.

Back in the cabin, you can hear the wind whistling an eerie high-pitched whine, like an insect, a child. *Why won't it stop? I was less sick when I fell pregnant,* Cowboy Hat says, *hardly even noticed and most people didn't realise 'cause I never showed until right at the end. Even then, Tulip was so early I had no idea she was coming. I swear she just jumped out. Afterwards I'd hear older girls talking about sickness, pain splitting them in two like an axe but I never felt any of that. Guess I'm paying for it now.* Ingénue stays perfectly still, not daring to say a word.

On green felt tables cards are laid out for bezique and *chinchón*. In the small library, people sit with the papers looking out through portholes at the steady line of the silver horizon. Downstairs in the bar, dancers perform the quickest of costume changes, from sailors and pirates to townsfolk and bandits, even rancheros. The men twirl the women and throw them up in the air so their skirts tumble down. Ingénue yawns: *Their showtunes aren't a patch on Eldorado's.*

Up on the top deck they watch passengers from the staterooms dressed for dinner in tuxedos and ball gowns. Waiters carry trays of tall mojitos and scooped out pineapples filled with rum. *See those men in tails and top hats, with the white gloves and silk scarves by the ice sculpture of the ship?* murmurs Cowboy Hat. *There, by the table with those sugar dolphins, two women standing next to the men. One with long diamante earrings and a tiger skin kinda wrap, the one next to her in plain black. That's not the wives, those two are together, same as us. Shall we go talk to them?* asks Ingénue. *Nah they'd never talk to the likes of us! Look we're about to land!*

The solider aimed and felt his arm begin to shake. He ground his teeth, willing his arm to stop and then found his legs shaking as well. It was dark, so he hoped none of the others would see. *Come on,* he told himself, *there's nothing to it, you've done this many times* and repeated in his mind all the things the commander had told them. His heart beat faster than ever. It banged inside his chest louder than gunfire. Sweat was trickling from his armpits into his shirt. His hands felt wet, the gun became slippery. Too slippery to hold, like a fish he had tried to catch as a boy. The fish had wriggled and slid from his hands. He'd been angry and picked up his father's rifle and shot into the river till the fish, several fish in fact, floated up, blood streaming out of them, the redness spreading across the surface. His father said *Don't waste bullets* and chuckled. He never knew if it was to share a joke or laugh at him.

Not now, **her** lips scarcely move, the words trail thin as smoke. She has withdrawn her hand. *I thought you weren't scared of anyone.* Ingénue's mouth is a dark cloud billowing back. By way of reply, Cowboy Hat rolls up her shirt lazily as if to scratch her belly, just high enough so that Ingénue can see the ridge of a scar. *Don't look round, those guys at the far table all carry* cuchillos. *I just want us to stay alive.* The waiter comes back and they order their favourite *mantecados* with a slice of *pastís de Turón*.

Walking back from the Festival del Fuego, they stop in a bar that's just a shack on the beach. Ingénue looks over the shoulder of each man who asks her to dance and winks at Cowboy Hat who tires of watching and catches her between dances. They dance together and the men, seeing Cowboy Hat knows the steps, leave them alone. A street seller wanders in offering them gardenias to throw at the feet of the singer as she walks between tables. Cowboy Hat buys a bunch. The singer gives her an appraising smile and stoops to pick up one of the flowers, pressing it to her face to inhale the scent. Ingénue throws her arm lightly around Cowboy Hat's shoulder. In a corner, the band play guitars and *charangos*. One man runs his stick along a horse's jawbone, catching on teeth that clatter in time to the beat.

When they come back to the hotel, the maid has arranged their clothes in a geometric pattern with what looks like a gardenia in the centre. That night, Cowboy Hat dreams a dead pigeon is stuck in the air con fan and no one can reach it to stop the stench. Ingénue dreams of a herd of skeletons galloping across the *campos*, yellow teeth gleaming, moonlit.

Ingénue wakes up from a bad dream. *I thought I'd lost you.* Cowboy Hat wipes her tears as they roll down her cheeks. *I know that dream, I had it too. Is this a dream as well then? If we both dreamt it, which is real? This is real, it's always this. But you'd say that if this was a nightmare too.*

What will you do when I'm old? *You are old.* I mean really old. *You are really old.* I mean really, really old. *I guess I'll really, really have to love you even more.*

Doesn't it bother you? Ingénue asks the Bearded Lady. *What, does it demean me, when they gawp, to be perceived as Other — is that what you want to know? You'd prefer me to put on a suit, work in a bank? I'd pass easily enough but I'd rather get paid for being a freak. I walk a hall of mirrors, parodying parody. Try it sometime. We all have to pay dues, even you, Ingénue.* The Bearded Lady, also known as Bear Woman for the thick black hair covering her face, has peeled off red leather gloves while speaking and bends down to unlace matching red boots. *You could travel back with us,* says Ingénue, less certain. *How sweet you are and it's true I haven't visited Eldorado in so long but the open road suits me. They're so self-congratulatory back there, always trying to prove they're right. I don't mean Dame Blanche of course, though I hear nowadays even she only talks of growing her* pimientos. *What tedium! Here people laugh or spit at me but I've grown such a pretty, such a sparkly carapace.*

Light snakes between trees, submerged by the river in spate. Red and gold streaks of light coil round their dark crowns.

When the storm dies down, the river reappears, now brown, now emerald. They pass boulders the size of countries beneath buffalo big clouds, trees steeple tall. Strewn like matches emptied from a giant pocket, pines litter the red earth. Like the curved blade of a skinning knife, the river cuts open the valley then vanishes. Ingénue waits for it to reappear but, after an unslept night, her eyelids grow heavy. She dreams she is driving the train. It begins to go faster but no matter how hard she pulls on the walking beam, she can't make it stop. She and Cowboy Hat both miss the river when it returns, a stream this time.

Over wide fields of red earth and yellow wheat, small planes spray a mist. In the distance, telegraph poles stand like gallows against a pale sky. Trees are ash white. Their shrivelled arms point at the moving train. Between each row new shoots of green are sprouting. They point as well. *I never knew the world could be so empty*, sighs Ingénue. Beside the skeleton of a shack, she sees a truck with its wheels gone, chassis sunk in the grass as if growing there. Cowboy Hat has squeezed her body between two crates and fallen asleep straight away while Ingénue wriggles, unable to get comfortable. She is tired of the shadowy scenery rushing past but can't tear her gaze away. The lights of faraway villages, the last orange rays of sun above hills and forests. The moon drops low and races alongside them as though trying to jump on.

All night the train whistles at every crossing. A mournful sound which wakes Ingénue while Cowboy Hat sleeps. A wheezing whistle. Calling and aching. Hooting and blowing. Tooting and ailing. Wheezing and wailing, ailing and wanting. Wishing all night.

Everyone fell in love with the young monk who came to assist Father Ignatius. When it snowed, he went outside hurling snowballs with the children and showing them how to build ice shanties and igloos. He took them down to the river in spring to wade and look for tadpoles, even gold; in summer they caught fireflies which they put inside bottles to make lanterns. *You must always let them go again*, he said.

Everyone agreed his eyes were the shape of *almendras*. Skin the colour of burnt toffee, voice soft as a girl's, they said. When he was found hanged in his cell in the autumn, no one could believe it. There was no note, no explanation. The oldest of the nuns had seen him burning something on the bonfire, letters or pages from a notebook. He lies near the river in unconsecrated ground, next to the graves of others, an even younger boy who once ran away, two girls who drowned themselves and an unbaptized newborn left in the woods during the fighting. No one blesses their graves yet each spring crocuses appear and all through summer every flower you can imagine, from bluebells to the tall stems of loosestrife, pokes up out of the earth.

When Cowboy Hat falls sick, Ingénue makes herself very small. *Have you done this before? No, but I once saw a village woman perform the same operation* and as Cowboy Hat coughs Ingénue dives in through her open lips. Once she has passed the biliary tree, having waded through sludge and across mud flats, on her way towards the duodenum, Ingénue dips unexpectedly into blackness. She floats slowly past clusters of coral and shimmering objects which twist through the dark even more slowly than her. Trailing like jellyfish or glasswort, figures swim towards her, glowing with a pale light. Ingénue no longer knows if she has entered Cowboy Hat's body or soul. The figures turn away before she can see their faces

Cowboy Hat raises herself onto her elbows and sits up for the first time in days. Her stomach is growling. *Is that Ingénue? This can't be happening.* Her throat burns with thirst. *Come back,* she calls and starts coughing again. Her shirt is drenched with sweat but she is afraid to take a sip of water. What if she drowns her lover?

Even a moth folds its wings. The smallest creature can retract momentary feet. Did I swim out too far? Was I leaning towards you? I am lost, unable to alter my shape, no case of glinting minerals wrapped around me. A door swings on hinges. It opens and closes. I must be a broken window, guts spilled, world blowing in. Am I ghost? Would a man ever think he was an over-ripe nectarine, seeping? Long after the well empties, when all the riverbeds are dry, I go on pouring.

Even though he knew it couldn't be her, when the boy heard the footsteps he hoped it was his mother, that she'd scoop him into her arms and say: *No more hide and seek now, time to come home for your bath*. Instead, as the footsteps came nearer, he heard a stranger's voice and in a flash of light from the torch saw the cream band of a nun's wimpole and her old face bending over him. Even though she spoke softly he screamed. He couldn't stop the sound. It left his body and was so shrill it only scared him more and then he couldn't stop shaking or screaming. He felt he'd wet himself even as the stranger reached for him through the dark.

She crouched down and held him wrapped in a woollen blanket, rocking him on her lap till, after some time, he stopped screaming. The blanket smelled soapy. He could see she had a brown rabbit with a ribbon round its neck in her hand and instead of talking to him she talked to the toy. *Poor rabbit, you must be tired, walking so far through the snow and I expect you got a bit scared alone in the dark.* She turned to the boy as though she had only just noticed he was there. *I need someone to help me look after this rabbit because he got lost in the snow. Do you think you could do that?* She handed him the toy. He nodded.

The walk down from the dugout took a long time. She held his hand part of the way and carried him for the last bit as he was falling asleep. At last they reached the main road where a truck was waiting. *I'm going to drive us to the priest's house*, she said. *There are some other children staying in the house too. You'll be safe there, all right?*

What Cowboy Hat remembers: *A nun came to visit. Sister, my Papa said to her, once upon a time there was a remedy for people — he nodded in the direction of my Mama — sick in the head. And do you know who ad-min-istered it? He began to laugh. An executioner! Chop, chop, no more stupid head! Roly poly, bang, bang, bang along the ground! He was* *still laughing when he called to me: Get over here, Big Ears! I swear that man had eyes in the back of his head. I'd been listening by the door, see. Bang! Bang! I shouted too, waving imaginary pistols in the air.*

He was drunk of course but I didn't care. I ran over. Mama was sitting at the table and to my surprise she kinda slumped forward and put her head in her hands. Her shoulders started heaving and I realised she was crying. Now she never did that. Most of the time she just looked cross or cursed when Papa told his jokes. The nun was asking me if I'd like to go away to stay with some other children. Papa had told me at the children's home the priest put his finger up the children's bum-holes to check if they did their business, so I said I wanted to stay at home, which made Mama cry even more.

Cowboy, sweetheart, don't you have any happy memories from your childhood?

At one stall, the bald-headed El Maestro Wu Wu sits, his eyes closed, hands upturned on the folding wooden table in front of him. A winding queue of people waits to hammer a silver nail into each outstretched palm. Sudden as a cuckoo clock, his eyelids open wide and, though Ingénue is standing some distance back, she feels his gaze fly out to hers. *Wouldn't you like to try?* he asks so softly it seems no one but her can hear. Both children and adults smash the nails into his hands in a kind of frenzy, sometimes exceeding the three turns they have paid for. Ingénue shakes her head. *Oh no I was only wondering…* El Maestro Wu Wu laughs sweetly and finishes her sentence: *You were wondering how to protect the cartilage. Yes. Ask my old comrade in arms from the palaces of toil about these lao gon points when you go home*, he says. *Give her my sincerest wishes.* Seeing Ingénue's confusion, Wu Wu adds: *Ask Dame Blanche.* And then his eyelids snap back shut.

Cowboy Hat, **asks** Ingénue, *doesn't Dame Blanche ever have a sweetheart? She must get lonely. Nah,* answers Cowboy Hat, *you can take the girl outta the city but you can't take the city outta her. When she feels the need, she goes into town. When the guards change over at the grave of the unknown soldier she usually finds somebody. Some handsome soldierbody. She doesn't want for company. Friendships, freedom — what more could a girl want?* Ingénue's black olive eyes darken. Deeper still. *Unless…* A menos que, shouts Cowboy Hat. *Unless…*

Ingénue pins Cowboy Hat against the door then moves her hand so slowly inside her that Cowboy Hat asks, *Where did you learn such tricks? From the best of course,* growls Ingénue. Cowboy Hat wonders about turning her round but finds she can't move. Ingénue has lifted her so that she hovers, limbs locked, waiting. Something has sapped all strength from her body. A heat, an aching? Por dios, *have a heart,* she gasps as Ingénue at last begins pushing faster.

When the river washed the bodies up, at first everyone thought it was a boy and girl, two newly weds, him in uniform, her in a bridal dress of tulle and lace. On closer inspection they realised it was two far younger girls. The 'bride's' dress was in fact from her holy communion and the 'groom' had stolen her brother's army trousers and jacket. It was thought they had jumped in holding hands. The letter they wrote and left behind said they were travelling to a place where they could be together, a place without boundaries or sleepless nights, somewhere swans and scorpions alike were free.

What Cowboy Hat wondered: I wish I'd seen their faces when Herr Hermann said that 'henceforth' space and time — 'by themselves' — were doomed to fade 'into the shadows'.

'Henceforth!' 'Into the shadows!' Of course two observers are gonna disagree on whether events are simultaneous — entering a barn or say dipping into the river — as though space and time could fit into one perspective. I wonder if old Hermann found consolation in all his measuring. But mainly I've been wondering why these folk would wanna pole-vault their way in and out of a barn in the first place. You'd think they'd have better things to do, ha ha. Did you know water remembers everything? I like thinking about water, takes my mind off… No rod — I'm thinking fishing rod as well as pole here — can be infinitely rigid either. But how are you going to measure difference? Which has the stronger force: the arc of someone's arm casting a rod or the fish's mouth tugging to free itself?

Copper wires like vines or rude gestures poke out of brick, stacks of breezeblock store the day's heat, a torn notice flutters down. Ingénue and Cowboy Hat throw down their bedrolls in a corner under the open sky. *'Está totalmente prohibido colocar tenderos para secar ropa en el exterior de las ventras por ser esto aniteistetico. Los empleados de la Comunidad están autorizados para retrer la ropa…' What is this place?* asks Ingénue. *They started to build here and they fled,* answers Cowboy Hat. *I miss our fields. I miss the fires at dusk — you could always find someone to talk to, someone sitting strumming. I miss Dame Blanche, miss Eldorado. I miss everybody. I want to go home. I thought you'd never ask.*

The first thing they see is the outline of tepees against a lavender dawn sky. At the gate, Cowboy Hat drives off to return the truck while Ingénue continues on foot. Here and there a fire is already lit, a blackened kettle whistling on its trivet. Smoke from inside yurts curls towards the soft clouds. Someone, unable to sleep any longer or who never went to bed in the first place, strums a banjo; oats are stirred in an enormous pot; children told to fetch clean bowls.

Ingénue finds herself smiling even though her rucksack and bags grow heavier with each step across the field. Soon her feet are wet with dew. Smoke puffs from the chimney in Dame Blanche's cabin. Prayer flags, silver and gold glittery flags flutter, bells tinkle; someone is feeding logs into the woodstove which powers the great sauna, a tall djembe drum wrapped in a rainbow-coloured scarf has been left out all night; someone else is pushing a wheelbarrow piled with groceries, sacks of beans, freshly baked loaves, punnets of blackberries. A new vegetable garden has been planted, runner beans interspersed with marigolds.

There as Ingénue had always known one day she would be, sprawled in a heap on their porch, a young woman dressed from head to toe in black leather is sleeping. Her jacket is studded all over, a skull on the back, ruby stones for eyes. *Who are you?* says the girl opening her eyes. *I'm Ingenue. I live here*, she answers. The girl gets to her feet. *You people should get on the grid, it's insane trying to find you. Where's my mother?*

Parte final

*in which past catches present by the tail having
first sprinkled a little salt on it*

"…my lady is definitely no lady
which is fine with me,
cause i ain't no gentleman."

Pat Parker, *Movement in Black, Collected Poems 1961-78*

Dear Mama,

Thank you for the horse you ~~craved~~ carved for me from lime wood. I put the red ribbon on its neck. At night it gallops and neighs just like you said. Mom and Dad got me a bicycle for my birthday. Love, Tulip XXX

Lil reaches across her for the packet, lights two cigarettes and hands one to Cowboy Hat. *I don't smoke anymore*, says Cowboy Hat taking it and coughing a little as she inhales to make the point. *There's a heap of things you don't do anymore.* Lil straddles her. With her free hand she pinches her nipple and bends down to kiss her on the mouth. The warm stream running through Cowboy Hat's limbs as she sinks back against Lil's satin sheets turns suddenly to ice. Through a trapdoor in the pit of her stomach she is falling, away from the brass bed, away from the sound of Lil's voice or the curl of smoke in her hand. *Ingénue.* She almost says it aloud.

There is a place along the river where every child knows never to swim. The water is so deep, so cold, it cuts through your skin and, where the currents meet, a muddy whirlpool sucks everything down as though the river had decided to claim all debris, broken twigs, pulled roots, scree and any floating animal and carry them to some hoard far below the black surface. There is little light and so the water — which normally shimmers, criss-crossed with sunlight catching in the nets and baskets of overhanging branches — is dull, dark with no scattering of light.

But that day the villagers ran to cross the river at any cost. Some still carried knapsacks, suitcases, linen bags filled with whatever they could find that seemed precious. A roll of bedding, a mirror, saucepan, an album of photographs. Others carried their children and it was them they threw first into the water. Some even pushed their neighbours out of the way on the bank. Just to get to the river first when they heard the soldiers behind them. Anything to flee the footsteps behind them.

Sometimes a lazy scratch is all it takes. Instant relief, satisfaction. But there's another itch you touch at peril. Better to poke a red ants' nest. No salve eases it. Ice might numb it for a while but even then numbness wears off all too soon. It makes you want to roll in gravel, bay at a frosty moon. You wish you could tear your skin off, turn inside out. But what good would that do? Your skin would only flap around your sides, a dry, ragged cloak tripping you up as you fled. Sometimes the itch is there for years on end, never letting you stay still. The way a splinter works its way below the surface, only deeper, leaving an unhealed sore, it lodges far below layers of each basal cell. Runs back and forth under the epidermis, alternating — front and back of one side, middle of the other — what you believe, however unlikely this must seem, countless sets of legs. On every foot tiny claws hook a purchase inside you. After a while people can tell.

This is what Cowboy Hat and Ingénue argued about: Who let the storm in. Who'd waited up all night, lit candles, cooked. Who hadn't asked for anyone to wait. Who never asks for anything. Who was so drunk they kicked the woodpile over. Who dissects details as if they were frogs. Who hurled the first insult, saying *burro*. Who, *por dios*, said who would end up like her father. Who said mother, which is worse. Who said who is aping pistol-waving *rancheros*, gunslingers. Who only muttered something. Whose eyes dart to another woman every time. Who always thinks she's right as though she was *canonizada*. Who jumped onto a table in Eldorado yelling: 'What's the point of loving women if they act like men?' toppled, still yelling — 'Men are kinder, donkeys too!' Who cheated. Whose hands reached over and whose fist opened like white *saguaro*. Who cheated. When is too late. Who broke whose heart.

Dear Mama,

Thank you for the riding boots. They fit me perfectly. I told Mom and Dad they were from Sister Asunta. I hope you won't mind but I didn't want to make them feel upset. What are you up to? Have you seen any racoons this year? Lots of love, Tulip XXXXXX

Can I offer you a *Slow Comfortable Screw up Against the Wall?* Someone in creaking leathers and jangling belt chains has slid onto the bar stool beside Ingénue. *Oh take no notice of Stud. Stud's harmless,* a second voice on her other side purrs. *Stud's exploring the dominant discourse. Thinks* I'm *wearing the trappings of submission to the hegemony but I could care less. Angel, by the way,* a lace glove is removed and a hand held out. Dame Blanche leans across the bar: *If these two get any more ironic, they'll iron themselves out. All the same,* Stud grumbles, *I hate to see a woman as* — Stud pauses — *electrifying yet autonomous on her own, if I had a woman half as beautiful I'd never leave her side.*

At closing time, disregarding all their protests, Dame Blanche swings Ingénue, fireman's lift style, over one shoulder and sets off across the fields. *There's something I've been meaning to say*, Dame Blanche begins under the starry sky once they're out of earshot of the small groups still round campfires. She stops, hearing Ingénue's snores louder now than a buffalo's.

In places where the water ebbed away you could cross the river on foot, making your way across silt to reach the faraway shore. Only, at any moment, the river might return. Nearby, in a small chapel of white stone, they kept a coffin ready. Here they laid the bodies of those washed up, leaving the coffin open in the hope someone would come by who could identify them. Soldier, donkey rider, child… A body couldn't be left out long, so a person might be buried before anyone knew their name. As a girl, Rocio came with her mother and aunts to put flowers on the altar and light candles. *Don't gawp.* Her mother pulled her past the coffin but Rocio always stole a glance at the body, its skin blue-red. Once, she noticed the garland of green algae in a man's hair.

I see the rivers when I go with you. Trees twist away to lean across the water, alder, oak, their branches almost brush the branches on the opposite bank. They dip their leaves in pockets of gold, shake, picking out fistfuls of green light. *Your silence canters beside me. I see horses loose as smoke in the distance.* At the water's edge, just as the light is fading a sounder of razorbacks runs past, sows in early autumn sable coats. Their tongues hanging out, fiery as sunset, heraldic red.

Where have you been? Ingénue asks when Cowboy Hat slides off her horse and shakes the dust from her clothes. Ingénue hates her for the dark smudge left by the sky over the land. For the emptiness of the porch all day. Cowboy Hat sees plates piled in the sink. Water not drawn from the well. She spits on the ground and strides over to the well. Ingénue follows. *Where have you been?* The wind toys with her voice. Cowboy Hat lowers the echoing bucket down.

Tell me about despair, says Dame Blanche, pouring Cowboy Hat a small Red Eye. *Made it m'self.* Cowboy Hat downs it in one go and indicates she needs another glass before answering: *You think you're wise to it, huh. The crumbs you left before got pecked by birds or else rain washed them clean, so this time you leave a trail of stones. Heavy enough, they shine in the rain, no bird can lift them in its beak. But is stone your friend or is it what grows, poking out from under it? Smelling of bad eggs? Spreading everywhere?* Primero plano *or* secundo? *Which? And what is it you were supposed to be looking for anyhow? A single flower? Red in the dark?* Ultimo plano? *Ghost weed, shardborn or carried by rain, a corpse plant which survives any understory, scaly, wax stems rising like swans.*

You can hear it coming. A low sound not so much like the wind, more surf, sea sucking on stones — sea wolf sucking on barnacle, whalebone. If you shine a torch you can see silver shapes in the distance rear and lobtail over the water. This is where tide meets current. Now the wave appears white-faced on the bend of the river. Foam spurting upwards. Fleet plumes of grey followed by almost see-through whelps. It doesn't yet roar. But its hoarse chuff grows louder until nothing's the same. The river's course has changed and now the water is flowing so fast it brings back everything it once carried out to sea. A red cap, children's shoes, whole trees, tea chests and chains, a boat sliced in half. Everything that drifted gently, now rushes past. The head of what looks like an elk?

The tablecloth has dark tassles which hang down like a fringe of vines at the entrance of a cave, through which you can see the feet of the adults, heels, boots, pacing back and forth. You can smell *pollo al herbes*, its onions and thyme. Under the table, no one remembers you are there. *Every butcher in town is closed yet we are having* pollo *today*, he says. *How* *many cocks have you sucked for this dinner?* She shouts back: *I've got children to feed. What do you bring home? Nothing!* Then him: *At least I don't fuck* colaboracionistas. A loud crash. Something has hit the floor but you can't see. A chair knocked over? The casserole? More footsteps. You push the yellow truck along the floor then knock it off its course with one hand and what you notice is how fast the wheels spin as it lies on its side. You try this again and again until you no longer hear what they are shouting.

What Ingénue might have added: *Sitting beside you watching clouds and stars I watched the clouds better and in between them darkness which seeps through everything. I saw moon separate from cloud — yolk from white — saw stars scooped in a pan, white gold shaken. I forgot to hurry, stared longer than I've ever done.*

Dear Mama,

How are you? Are you still carving things? I wish I could do some painting but I have to study for my exams. I am still riding and have now learned some jumps. I am also on the ice hockey team and I won a silver medal for free style swimming. I think I'd like to become a vet. Did you know vets have to learn how to treat humans but doctors don't have to know about animals? So I think it's better to be a vet but Dad says doctors are more respected. I hope your new house is nice. Do you live in it alone? I hope you are not lonely. I hope I will see you again soon. I could show you the stable where I go riding. Love you, Tulip XX

You can usually tell when a bear is going to die. It's not only the gaunt frame, joints poking through fur, or the look in its eyes. But animals like people can surprise you with their tenacity, a will to live stronger than suffering. Bears heal even from gunshot wounds once they have denned.

Some stories end mid-sentence, some crest. Some scatter in every direction, numerous channels running off before you can stop them. Others peter out leaving a ridge but no longer supporting the clusters of small life they carried. Some grasses, pheasant's tail and even wild iris, survive with little or no water. Then unexpectedly the rains return; everything changes once more.

Towards the end of summer the market stalls fill with chestnuts, milkcaps and russet *boletos*. Storms break every day. *I can't find the little beach we swam from only a few weeks ago,* Ingénue stamps her foot. Water stings her skin with cold as she wades in but she carries on swimming out to a submerged willow. When she clambers out she is shivering so hard she can't dry herself. She is still shivering that night, the next day and the day after that. Cowboy Hat opens the bottle of mescal she's been saving for winter and rubs the clear liquid into Ingénue's skin. It doesn't help.

Where crystals touch they bond together, squeezing the air between them to the surface or into bubbles. With every breath, Ingénue feels icy slivers fill her lungs. *So small you can't see them*, she thinks. Soon — crystals packed closer and closer — vapour will freeze inside her. Solid. Sharp. *I'm turning to glass,* she laughs, *everyone will see through me.* She tries to remember something. *Sage*, she rasps, *top left pocket*. Voice barely audible as Cowboy Hat rummages in Ingénue's medical bag. *Three minutes. Infuse.*

I'm used to turning slowly under a carapace of cloudy ice. Up there her voice is a saw creaking in and out. Everything is too bright, cracking with badly needed light. It is the sun, drilling a burr hole in dura mater. Down here you hide behind logjams, bury yourself in mud to stay out of riffles until rain and melting snow return, as bubbles of oxygen flit through cattails, eelgrass. What will she do if she can't hear *me? Up sticks? Pull down her ice shanty and move on. How do I let her know I'm on my way?*

When Ingénue woke up, her shirt was soaked through. She knew the fever had gone but felt too weak to get up, though her throat was parched. She called out but there was no answer. Hours later she woke again and saw it was dark outside. She called out again. Towards morning she heard voices, laughter and someone, maybe even Cowboy Hat repeatedly shushing the others. The door to the cabin was opened. There was a crash, then a thud as someone fell in.

The soldiers had ransacked the houses so there was little left in the larders. In places, a handful of flour had spilled out of a sack leaving a trail as it was dragged along the floor. That was enough to make a *pastel.* There were radishes, green tomatoes and *frijoles* the soldiers had not bothered to snatch. Sometimes a knocked-over jar of pickles, olives or stuffed *berenjenas.* If the glass was broken in many pieces you had to be careful not to swallow any. Women's and children's clothes hung untouched in wardrobes. Of no use to soldiers. Wrapped in a few layers, Sister Asunta slept in beds imagining the warmth of those who had left them suddenly. When she came across bodies still lying where they had fallen, if the smell was not too strong, she knelt to say a quick prayer before checking if any coins or gold chains remained, then went on her way.

No, don't tell me, says Dame Blanche and whistles. Cowboy Hat slurs: *I don't care about this*, indicating the plates in pieces, jagged waves sticking up all over the floor. *Don't sit down, she broke the chairs as well. I can mend those, only she said this time she ain't coming back.* Dame Blanche hesitates. *This probably isn't the right time, but I gotta tell somebody.*

She waves a hand in front of Cowboy Hat's face, on her finger an enormous ring with clusters of stars circling a moon. *Who'd have thought after all this time? I've got a fee-ancay!* Cowboy Hat stares blankly. *What, too traditional?* Dame Blanche carries on. *They're* marcasitas, *not diamonds. I can't wait for you to meet him. He's been digging over my cauliflower patch. Not that I can't do it myself. He's beautiful, like a faun, kinda muscular and… Cheap,* mutters Cowboy Hat, *I thought you liked your freedom. Oh don't be such a sourpuss. Ingénue will be back when she's cooled off. What did you do to make her so mad anyhow? No, don't tell me. I'm not listening to anything* triste *today!* sing-songs Dame Blanche over her shoulder. *Take Ingénue's side, everyone always does,* Cowboy Hat calls from the doorway, then staggers back inside and passes out.

When a body is re-assembled each bone (206 of them, if all were to be found) is carefully placed. What joy, what a sense of satisfaction for those who have worked long hours when a scrap of cloth — say, yellow *franela* — is found and fits the missing person's description. Someone can be identified at last. Without the meat and potatoes there is no narrative, only an anonymous jumble of limbs, or rather parts of limbs (the scaphoids, fibulas) in numbers which would overwhelm most people.

It's obvious when you think about it. There's nothing more to fear from the dead. It's the loss of distinguishing marks which terrifies. And yet, in or out of love, after the initial swelling of bodily tissues, as a person passes from excitement through to the next stage, heart rate and circulation of blood increasing, respiration elevated, as they are nearing climax through an almost random sequence of involuntary grimaces and vocalisations, it's the exact opposite of individuality or separate consciousness their mind craves. During those euphoric convulsions what it yearns for — and reaches — is a kind of oblivion, *la pequeña morte.*

Dear Mama,

I guess you may not receive this letter as you did not reply to my last one or the one before and that is not like you. We have moved house and since Sister Asunta died no one can tell me where you live. At first I thought maybe you had forgotten me or started a new family. Mom and Dad say you moved and did not leave a forwarding address. Usually they tell the truth about everything but when I ask about you they look at each other and say nothing.

I wish you had been at Sister Asunta's funeral. Instead of flowers from a shop, everyone brought wild flowers or herbs and the coffin was completely green and smelt lovely with all the lavender and rosemary and bay. Except I don't like sage because it's too bitter.

I didn't really say goodbye to Sister Asunta except at the funeral but Mom says she had a good death because she died in her sleep. I wonder if it hurts when you die. I hope it didn't. I hope it's like sinking into a feather pillow and everything getting softer and lighter. I have dreams where I fly above our house. It's fun and I am really light. I look down and see Mom planting nasturtiums and Dad reading the paper. I see my school and the tennis courts and the shopping mall. Once, I flew so high I brushed past a big bird and then I saw you. You were riding a horse. You were a brown dot on the horizon as small as an ant or a bug but I knew it was you and I woke up smiling. Love you always, Tulip X

In one village, towards the end of summer, vines turn the colour of rust and flame. Mist rises over them like smoke. Since all the radios have been requisitioned, no one knows if the war is over or which side has won. The soldiers quartered in the priest's house grow restless, uncertain if they should prepare to retreat or celebrate as victors. They have finished every last drop of wine they could get their hands on in any case. The air is frosty till noon, when the sun regains its strength. The soldiers run down to the river, shouting, stripping off to bathe, splashing in the icy foam.

This would be the moment, while they are naked and unarmed, to creep up from behind the trees on the river bank and shoot each of them as they laugh in the water. But some of the children have jumped in after them and are splashing too and this saves the soldiers.

At the establishment known as Villa Joy, Sister Asunta is balancing uneasily on an embroidered cushion of damson brocade. She blanches as a nun walks in carrying a tray. But it's only as the young woman approaches with mint tea and *pastelitos* that Sister Asunta notices the peachy layer of foundation on her cheeks. She blushes realising — oh rookie mistake — that it is one of Mercedes' *lupas*. Another girl dressed as a nurse follows carrying a freshly filled *narghile*. Mercedes shoos them away and waits patiently for her guest to compose herself. *I imagine you must be* in extremis *to come here,* she says carefully. *I'm not afraid of death,* begins Sister Asunta.

When she has finished speaking, Mercedes, who has been laying out cards embellished with pictures of kings and queens, horned *bisontes*, the moon and stars, a plough and piglets rooting, then a hanged man, looks up. Her eyes are deep lavender, the blue of bruises, of a sky just before sunset. *We're not as different as you think. Men talk to my girls because they don't consider them to be of consequence. They speak into a mist, wandering through a dream. You and I both know so much but are able to prove very little. I can arrange… I have contacts, who will mete out punishment without asking a single question. How exactly do you want me to help you?* Sister Asunta shakes her head. *I see. You don't want to perpetuate the cycle.* Mercedes turns over the corner of another card. Puts it straight back, face down. *They say you prepare potions. Yes but oblivion isn't discerning. To erase memories such as yours you have to forego happy memories at the same time. Is that really what you want? I want to stand in front of Our Dear Lord with a mind clear of these thoughts. I want to forgive.*

When the nun has gone, Mercedes lights a cigarette and lays out the cards again. Death, the stooping skeleton, scythe grasped in bony fingers, which frightens so many of her clients until she explains it does not necessarily mean physical death, appears straight away. It sweeps aside everything in its path, skulls, golden crowns, caged doves. You have to consider the surrounding cards, she always tells clients, it depends whether you stand before the calamity of figures falling from an Open Window or walk between wounding blows in the Forest of Knives, if you can draw on the strength of *Bisonte*, the endurance of coupled Swans. *So what next?* she says to Death.

The coyote's call is higher pitched than the bark or gekker of an urban fox, higher than a vixen's scream, she'd know the difference. Something wakes Ingénue. She tells herself it was glass, a bottle kicked across the pavement in those last moments before dawn breaks. Buses, dustcarts, the city is already on the move, before she has even opened her eyes. Aloud, she says: *I dreamt I was still with Cowboy Hat.* Her lover, awake now, turns to her, complaining, *Who the hell is he?* Ingénue sits up, tall as a pine, every needle pointing skyward. *She, who the hell is she?* It is one ending. Or beginning of sorts.

What Sister Asunta lay thinking: Closer to the dead than the living, these days I feel my thoughts dispersing like dandelion seeds. My back aches after a day's work, still I'm grateful when I can be in the garden away from adults with their intrusive, inane chatter. And it's only sometimes after a day's digging, of children smelling of grass, who tug on my habit, begging a go of fork and trowel, of my hands uprooting ivy, dandelion, burweed, earth deep under my nails — on those nights I touch myself and sleep sweetly again. But now I stand in the yew-shadow, the Redwood-shadow, blowing smoke rings like a young girl still afraid of being caught. My throat burns and the dream won't shrivel and curl and in the dream it's always me who holds the machete.

The first thing Claribel had done, after they left her face down in the sand, was kill the mule. They had shot it many times, deliberately avoiding the head or heart so that it lay whimpering and twitching on its side. They had done this to terrify her but kept her alive for sport. There was a small knife tucked into a pocket of her saddlebag, which they hadn't noticed when they tipped the contents out. They'd taken her water and her money. *What did you ever do to anybody?* she said, raising the animal's head onto her thigh before she cut its throat.

Gifts Cowboy Hat gave Ingénue: lacy parasol (adapted by Ingénue for use as a lampshade), snake-head ankle bracelet, silver hip flask. Earrings: feather dream-catchers, amber (green, dangling and studs), ruby hearts, stars. Pearl-handle pistol (traded by Ingénue with a patient for a bone-handle hunting knife), red cowboy boots (snake skin), *mascada* (leopard skin motif, red with black), keepsake box (carved by Cowboy Hat). *Chicha* (home-made, poured by Ingénue onto the compost). Books: *Book of Shadows — Sacred Wicca*, *Animales Peligrisos* (stolen), *Blue Eagle's Secrets of Healing*, *Remedios A Base Hierbas Para Dolores Y Molestias* (used), *The Golden Age of Detective Fiction* (second hand). A banjo.

Gifts from Ingénue to Cowboy Hat: small rosewood plane, bone-handle hunting knife, beeswax polish (home-made, no turpentine), whiskey, reproduction of Leyster's Tulip (mounted and framed), gold watch chain (family heirloom), boots (classic tall shaft, black), batwing summer chaps, new beaver fur felt Stetson (after she stamped on the old one in an argument), wintergreen balm, muslin bag of star anise, hardcover edition of *Kit Carson's Cowboy Annual 1954*, saddle blanket (woven) and *cantina,* Minkowski's *Space and Time* papers on relativity (third edition), *Los Mejores Poemas de Amor* (new), forgiveness, melody.

Claribel is distracted. Someone calls out: *It's those homos living in tepees on the edge of town. We don't want our children learning about* sexo and género. *What am I supposed to do if I can't smack her? I can't afford to buy my boy a PlayStation.* Usually she relies on her lined face, silver braid and low voice to carry authority with parents. *We're talking about how to keep children safe*. She exhales before continuing: *We start by teaching them to respect their own bodies.* It isn't the derisory laughter throughout the hall which follows her words like a swarm of bees that distracts her.

After all these years how can she be sure? Many people have odd sizes of ears, not as many perhaps as those with differently-sized feet, that's more common. He is standing at the back of the hall with his wife, having come in late. What's more surprising is that it hasn't happened sooner. She saw him only once, when he would have been a boy himself, can't remember what the others looked like, wouldn't have remembered him if it hadn't been for the ears. Maybe it was a brother, a cousin of his. She knows only that one of his ears, the left one, long-lobed, reddish at the edges, then paler till the small dark cave inside, stuck out further than the other ear when for a moment she opened her eyes to see whose turn was next.

I may have told a few white lies. They may not have been exactly white. I may have coloured something in. I never bulldogged. Never won at anything in my life. Rode rodeo once or twice. Or once. There was one woman I followed, went by the name of Bonnie Blue Racer. She could flounce and side-saddle but she didn't always like to, so she straddled and taught herself the under-belly crawl at speed. I could never have impressed Blue if I'd tried and it was only my kid I ever wanted to impress. Exactness is a science and I'm no alchemist. What's the opposite of a light bulb? Some say a pomegranate. And snow follows quickly if you don't count to a hundred. A few degrees north of truth, a little south of mundane is where you'll find me.

When she heard the soldiers were already at the bridge, one day away, Rocio's mother ran to gather up all the gold coins left by her grandfather. She placed them inside a saucepan and took the heaviest hammer out to the woods behind the house. She and Rocio battered the saucepan, taking turns to beat the metal harder than they had ever struck anything in their lives, battering and banging with all the rage and fear they possessed till the pan was flat, a grey plate with no hint of gold.

They hid the pan in the embers of the fire-pit behind the house. When the soldiers came they slaughtered the one chicken she hadn't caught in time to pass on to cousins and she watched as they roasted it over the fire they'd built on top of the old pan buried in ash and dirt.

What Ingénue whispered: *If at a moment before dawn, when the dark gathers everything to itself, your soul should stray, if when the dark, reluctant to let go before that first intimation of light, first birdsong note or weak grey sun, tightens its hold; if just then your soul should stray too far, it can't come back. It won't return to the light's bustle, the opening of shutters or the scrape of chairs, cock's crow, engine's purr or the slosh of water. No kiss on the eyelid, no tug on the arm can bring you back, though your face might look smooth in repose. Not even the angriest call could wake you. Not the simple smell of café with scalding leche or your favourite pasteles brought on a* *tray to bed. Don't be afraid, I'll wrap my arms around you, I won't let you slip away from me. I'll hold you closer than the dark.*

When you wake up, you are thirty years older. The horses are gone. Looking out from the porch, you sigh with relief. You hear the thwack-thwock of an axe. *I dreamt we were dancing*, you call. You are certain you remember how to do a lock-step. Are you still dreaming? The birch wood is there, its white rows, like a division of infantry making its way to the end of the world.

Dear Mama,

I thought if I wrote to you it might help me remember things. The other day I found some pictures I'd done. Remember you taught me to write my *M*s all pointy because you said they were two blue mountain peaks either side of a valley and that *M* was a Most Important Letter as it was the first letter of Mama. The other Terribly Important Letter too of course was *T* for Tulip. The line at the top was the flower on a stem, you said. I drew my flowers like that for ages until Claribel, the lady who came for Art Club, brought in a bunch of actual tulips. She put them in a vase next to a coffeepot, with an orange and a pile of books all arranged on an embroidered tablecloth. She said it was *naturaleza muerta* and we had to sketch it and then paint it. I used to love her lessons but I've got exams now so I haven't been painting anything. I hope you are well. Are you still carving shapes? I hope this letter reaches you. Everyone calls me Teresa now but you can still call me Tulip if you prefer. Love, T.

When Mercedes heard the man calling to her, she thought her legs would give way beneath her. She stopped on the path and could not move. He was old she realized and thought perhaps she would have a chance against him in a fight. He was waving his arms, beckoning her over and calling in a dialect so thick she could barely understand what he was saying. She thought she heard the word *frijoles*. Something in his manner made her stand still even as he made his way from the porch of his house towards her. *Maybe I'm too tired to run anymore*, she reasoned with herself. She had thought all the houses were empty. He took her by the hand and led her to the rickety table on the porch. He was saying something about the legs of the table and he bent down, with some difficulty, to place a stone under one of the legs. He motioned for her to sit on the bench. As she did an unexpected relief made her muscles ease for the first time in days but she kept one hand on her saddlebag. He left her sitting there while he went back into the house.

When he came out again, he was carrying a bowl of steaming beans cooked in what looked like tomato with garlic. He placed the bowl in front of her and handed her a spoon. As she started to eat hungrily, she looked up and saw he was watching her. A smile had spread over his face so broad it made his leathery creases even deeper.

After her mother's funeral, what Cowboy Hat recalls: *Since my Mama was dying, I couldn't exactly pull my hand away. She'd gulped down the* anis *I brought her — I didn't think it mattered now. Greedy. Suddenly I knew what she was up to. Her fingers — thin as chalk sticks, I was scared I'd snap them — flipped my hand over palm up. Like I was her open book. If* El Señor Todopoderoso *admits me to his kingdom, I will pray for you, she said. She was relishing this moment. You may be* deshonrada *but it's not too late to find* un hombre. *There! What a tall man, look! Handsome, dark.* Jesús y María, es un negro! *She'd seen Dame Blanche, so I knew she could see my whole life laid out there. Mama shuddered. And that's,* Dios te perdone, *your* fruto de amor, *your bastard, she said. She spat but without her old skill and a white glob stayed on her chin, catching on the hairs. I looked away. Then: All these* *broken lines are the* chicas *you've been chasing.* ¡Uf! *More saliva — white as snake spit on thistles in spring. Not one of them is your intended, your* destinada, a menos que, *unless — she dropped my hand to fall on the sheets, adding that she was tired. You never met my mother. She had the gift. But she was sly.*

Everybody looks below the surface hoping they'll find some meaning, some remnant of a wreck, cargo of lost gold, if they just look hard enough and deep, when all they need is a glance. It's enough to brush the surface lightly with a gaze, here, where a fish can jump through air or a bird dive under water, where light breaks and joins itself.

Imagine gazing at the green surface of the water. Your face, the trees, mountains and sky are there. One sigh of the wind is all it takes and everything's gone — face, trees, stone, clouds — and you have to wait till it comes back the same way you wait for your pleasure, slippery as a fish, to leap between worlds out of the water, through air, and back again.

Notes

p. 37: Cowboy Hat's musings were inspired by Hermann Minkowski's theories on relativity and the space-time dimension.

p. 42, 44: Ingenue's thoughts were inspired by the poems of Frances Pessoa, written in his persona Alberto Caeiro.